BURNING WOOD

Dermot McGuigan

Prism Press

Published in 1979 by

PRISM PRESS,
Stable Court,
Chalmington,
Dorchester,
Dorset DT2 0HB

ISBN 0 904727 78 5 Hardback
ISBN 0 904727 79 3 Paperback

Printed in England by
UNWIN BROTHERS LIMITED,
The Gresham Press, Old Woking, Surrey.

Contents

Introduction

The number of people using wood as a fuel is growing at a remarkable rate. The reason is not hard to find. The average fuel inflation rate in the UK has been running at about 25% per annum for the past six years leaving many householders and farmers with crippling heating bills to pay. The home-owner who has access to fuelwood and burns it in an efficient woodstove and multi-fuel boiler can considerably reduce the annual heating bill. Indeed there are some who no longer have a fuel bill, particularly those who own a woodlot or have an arrangement with the Forestry Commission to remove the waste after tree felling, called the 'lop and top'. Many farmers are now harvesting straw which would otherwise be burnt in the field and are using it instead in multi-fuel central heating boilers.

Energy Crops

Trees are more than just beautiful, they are also excellent solar collectors. They collect the solar energy by means of photosynthesis and store the bulk of that energy as wood. The outcome of this natural cycle is that summer sunshine is stored for winter warmth. Besides, trees are good friends to have around, birds and other wildlife live among them, they give shelter and can give wood. After felling and air-drying, the wood will keep for years without losing energy.

Plant fuels are generally called biofuels to distinguish them from fossil fuels. The difference between the two is that the first is renewable and can be grown locally whereas the second is non-renewable and is usually controlled by centralised bodies. Any crop which grows may be air-dried and used as fuel for a multi-burning boiler. The economies of using straw, and crops such as oil seed rape, as fuel work out very well. It has been estimated that in Britain alone up to 3.4 million tons of straw are burnt in the field each year, the fuel equivalent of which is 1.5 million tons of coal. No farmer will want to waste this potential fuel if he is shown how he may benefit from burning it in a multi-fuel boiler.

Is There Enough Fuelwood?

Obviously woodburning is impractical for most people living in cities or treeless areas. Aside from that the fact is that there is a very definite surplus of wood for burning in rural areas; dead elm trees, forestry waste, wind-blown trees, clearings from woodlots, coppices and hedgerows, etc.

At the time of writing there are only about 30,000 wood-stoves in use in the UK, there is room for considerably more than that. Dutch Elm disease has left about 11.5 million dead trees in the UK. Instead of burning it where it is felled why not use it as a fuel? It burns well and once air-dried will keep for years. The sizeable waste from public and private forestry has yet to be used efficiently. Left-overs from the furniture and timber trades amount to a sizeable quantity of wood. All these various sources make for a glut of fuel just waiting to be used.

We have a long way to go before reaching it but there is a limit to how many wood burning appliances this country can afford to fuel. Whilst no accurate details are available this figure has been put above the one million mark. After that, demand for wood could cause the abuse of living woodland. This social disease is happening right now in some parts of the world where those who depend upon wood for cooking have stripped the land of trees. The outcome is that without trees the land loses its moisture and the soil erodes away leaving a dustbowl where woodland once was. And so, if you burn wood be sure to plant trees! Indeed we are fortunate that trees can be grown for there is no way that coal or oil can be similarly replaced.

A Clean Fuel

Air-dried wood is practically a smokeless fuel when burnt in an efficient closed stove. The pollution caused by burning wood is far less significant than that caused by fossil fuels because wood contains only a fraction of the sulphur and oxides of nitrogen found in coal and oil. In burning, both biofuels and fossil fuels release carbon dioxide into the atmosphere. Carbon dioxide causes a heat trapping green-house effect in the atmosphere but the beauty of biofuels (as opposed to coal, oil etc.) is that they only release as much carbon as they absorb when growing and so a balance is maintained. The difficulty arises when massive quantities of age-old coal and oil are burnt in the space of a few short years hence releasing sufficient carbon dioxide to cause atmospheric pollution.

Another aspect to this is that if left to rot on the forest floor, wood will release just as much gas and heat as if the same wood was burnt! Therefore it can justly be claimed that burning wood creates no pollution and as a fuel it creates an excellent ecological balance, that is assuming there is at least as much growing wood as there is being burnt.

Questions are often asked about the use of biofuels and smokeless zones in the UK. Aside from the major conurbations and a few small towns this is really a non-problem. Smoke control zones hardly affect the countryside at all. The present legislation was calculated to stop coal smoke. Details of smoke controlled areas are available from the Department of the Environment.

Wood — an Economic Fuel

That fuel prices over the past six years have risen at an alarming rate is beyond dispute. A recent HMSO publication on energy confirms that costs have risen at an average rate of 25% per annum over the past few years. True, prices have reached a temporary plateau for the present, conservation and cut-back measures have caused a glut on the oil market. This glut really hides the potentially dangerous situation where Arab states and President Carter feel that a real gap in the supply and demand of oil is likely to arise in the 1980's. Sheikh Yamani of Saudi Arabia, said in an interview in May 1978 that the current oil price stability is unlikely to last longer than 1980.

North Sea oil and gas certainly are a bonanza but the cost of extraction is high and the end product will not be any cheaper than it is now. North Sea oil production will peak about 1985 and after that we will need additional imports, so will many other nations at the same time, and the likely result will be another inflationary spiral. How long natural gas will be in abundance is a debatable issue, there are great disparities between estimates made by the Gas Board and independent energy authorities. Suffice it to say that as a non-renewable resource its price must begin to reflect its irreplaceable value. About ten years ago Holland developed its natural gas resources in the same way as Britain is currently doing. Holland now finds itself in the unenviable position of having to import gas to fill the gap between supply and demand.

Cost of Fuel relative to 1971

Year	Coal	Oil	Natural Gas	Electricity
1971	1.000	1.000	1.000	1.000
1972	1.109	1.056	1.000	1.000
1973	1.242	1.578	1.000	1.033
1974	1.529	2.345	1.075	1.061
1975	2.184	2.907	1.466	1.370
1976	2.322	3.078	1.607	2.031
Average Annual Increase	26%	41.4%	12%	20.6%
Overall Average Annual Increase		25%		

Coal is in abundance, it is also expensive and so are miners as we were reminded during the three-day week. The image of nuclear power as a universal energy panacea has become somewhat tarnished.

Wood burning will not solve this nation's energy problem but, if it can keep many a home warm, the strongest case for using waste wood and straw as a fuel is that it is available. Stoves are cheap, multi-fuel burners are more expensive than ordinary central heating boilers but they usually pay back their cost within a few years. In many cases the only price to pay for wood as a fuel is the cost of bringing it home and cutting it. From the point of view of health it can be a net gain for the office worker who benefits from the exercise and fresh air. Even buying wood at £10 a ton makes sense as the cost comparison chart below shows. The most striking thing about the chart are the costs shown for wood and straw.

COST COMPARISON CHART — Winter 77/78

Fuel	Cost	Efficiency	Cost per kWh
Electricity	2.65 p kWh	100%	2.65 p
Electric night storage	1.29 p kWh	100%	1.29 p
Natural gas	22.8 p therm*	70%	1.11 p
Natural gas	15.3 p therm	70%	0.75 p
Oil	37.5 p gallon	70%	1.12 p
Paraffin	46.5 p gallon	92%	1.09 p
Coal (bituminous)	£2.40 cwt	25% open fire	2.27 p
		65% closed fire	0.87 p
Wood	£10.00 ton+	65% woodstove	0.36 p
Wheat straw	£12.00 ton+	65% multi-fuel boiler	0.35 p

* Cost of first 52 therms used each quarter
+ These costs would be much lower if the user gathered his own fuel and did not cost his time.

The Many Ways of Burning Wood

The aesthetic attraction of the open fireplace is strong but in reality it is a way of sending your money up in smoke. The reason being that only a mere 10 or at most 20% of the heat is radiated into the room, the rest goes straight up the chimney. It is possible to increase the useful heat output from an open fire. One way of doing this is by bringing the air required for combustion from outside the building rather than creating a draught inside the room as air is drawn to the fire. A second method is to use a special heat circulating fireplace which convects hot air around the room. A similar effect can be achieved by using hollow steel pipes as a grate, air in the pipes can be heated by natural convection or the air can be forced by a fan. The benefits from an open fire can be increased by the addition of a back-boiler for domestic water heating. With any of these methods one can continue to enjoy the blaze and to some extent cut down on the waste.

I should mention here that most fireplaces in the UK are designed to burn coal and not wood. A coal fire will, of course, burn wood but to get the same heat from wood one would need to use four times as much wood as coal. Pound for pound wood has about half the calorific value of coal, moreover as its density is low it occupies about twice the space of coal. As such one would not get very warm burning wood in the small grate of a coal fireplace. The answer is to increase the size of the hearth, or better still, forget about the inefficient open fire and use a wood-burning stove instead.

When it comes down to serious efficient heating then a good solid woodstove or boiler is the answer. With such appliances efficiencies of 60 or 70% are normal, indeed some manufacturers claim stove efficiencies of up to 80%. In practice, this means that for every hundredweight of wood burnt in a stove one would need to burn at least six hundredweight in an open fire just to get the same heat output! With a stove there is far less work to do chopping wood, fuelling the fire and cleaning it out. But, most important, the cost of running a stove — as opposed to an open fire — is reduced by up to 80%. It is much easier to regulate the heat output from a stove than from an open fire. The wide range of stoves and wood-fired cookers available today ensure that there is likely to be one to suit every taste and pocket.

Until recently the idea of using a wood or straw-fired 'multi-fuel' boiler was virtually unheard of in Britain even though such appliances have been produced in Europe for up to forty years. Today there are eight makes available. Multi-fuel heaters provide central heating from a variety of solid fuels such as wood, coal and bales of straw. They operate well in conjunction with an existing central heating system. Some multi-fuel heaters can also be adapted to operate on oil, gas and even electricity. Such units and combinations can be controlled to burn oil or gas first thing in the morning to take the chill out of the house before the first solid fuelling takes place. The fuel adaptability ensures that the cheapest fuel available may be used. Another advantage is that many of these boilers will take logs up to 3 ft long which means less chopping and fuelling.

The Open Hearth

Violent fires soon burn out themselves

Shakespeare

The open fireplace is little more than an expensive luxury. True, it gives a good focal point in the living room. A blazing fire also gives an illusion of warmth and comfort, an illusion that can be shattered if your legs take the brunt of the draught of cold air drawn by the fire. Basically the open fire is not a home heater, at least not unless it is kept going around the clock.

Fireplace Inefficiency

It is generally agreed that the efficiency of a typical fireplace used today is between -5% and +15%. Nearly all the heat that goes into the room is radiant heat, the bulk of the convected heat being drawn straight up the chimney. It was the recognition of this that led to the first development of box stoves some 500 years ago, a development that is not surprising as an open fire consumes 3 to 10 times more wood than a stove just to give the same heat output. It follows that fuelling a wood stove requires considerably less effort.

A conventional fireplace can cause an overall heat loss. The reason being that the fireplace and chimney outlet are left open even when the fire is dying and out, and this results in warmed air inside the house being drawn up the chimney. An experiment was carried out on a house in the US with gas-fired central heating and an open fireplace. When the thermostat was in the room where the fire was, the radiant heat affected the thermostat causing a reduction in the heat supplied to the rest of the house by the gas burner. Hence less gas was used but the house remained colder. But when the thermostat was in a different room a net heat loss was recorded. In other words slightly more gas, 2%, was used with the fire than without. The reason for this was the loss of centrally heated air up the chimney.

Some tests using open fireplaces burning coal around the clock have been shown to have efficiencies of 10% to 25%. If the fire is kept going there is less loss due to the heating and cooling of the chimney also there will be no draught up the flue when the fire is dead. But these figures are really academic as nobody is going to the trouble of trying to keep an open fire going continuously, and anyway we are dealing with wood and not coal.

More Heat from Your Fire

An effective way to increase the heat output from an open fire is to use a tube grate. Such devices are readily available in the US but not so in the UK. However it is possible to make your own. A tube grate is a simple device which draws cool air in at the bottom and expels hot air out at the top. The fire burns on the steel tubes which become very hot and in turn conduct heat to the circulating air. Natural convection can be used to circulate the air but the tube grate will give a greater heat yield if the air is forced by means of a fan.

The materials required for the construction of this heat circulator are simple and can be found in any scrap yard. Bicycle handlebars and tubular chair frames are just the thing. Two handlebars can form the base upon which is welded 5 or 6 curved sections of steel tube. The heat saving unit can then be welded solid or bolted together. To increase the efficiency a 20 to 40 watt fan may be used to circulate air through the pipes. You will need to add ducting to the base of the pipes and also ensure that the fan is offset to one side of the fire.

An advance on the tube grate principle is the circulating fireplace. These are more difficult for the individual to make

The Jetmaster Principle
All 'Jetmaster' units (including Hex) use heat from the back of the fire which, in an ordinary fireplace, is absorbed by masonry or lost up the chimney. The flow of air from inlet to outlet and its changing temperature is illustrated in this cut-away of the built up form: the standard is the same, but with no gather.
1   *Air at room temperature*
2   *Drawn into inlet*
3   *Passes through heating duct*
4   *Enters superheating chamber*
5   *Is heated to maximum temperature over the hottest part of the fire*
6   *Forced into hot air duct and expelled through jet or louvre into the room*
7   *Hot air rises and circulates to create 'round-the-room' comfort*
8   *Damper control lever regulates rate of burning*
9   *Fumes into chimney*
10 *Firegrate (or baseplate where fitted).*

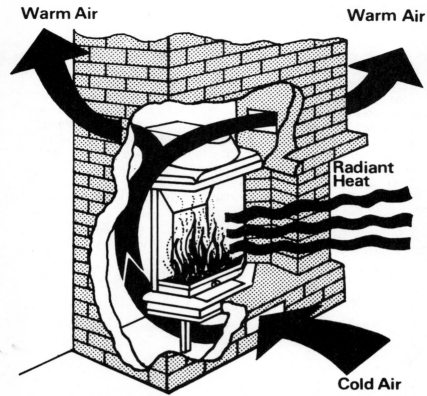

Warm Air

Warm Air

Radiant Heat

Cold Air

Diagram showing the principle of the Dovre fireplace imported by Strax Distribution Limited.

but fortunately there are commercial models available. The fireplace is a double walled unit which draws cool air in to be heated by the fire surround and then directs the hot air back into the living room. Such units are designed to fit tightly into existing open fireplaces - - or they can be freestanding — and some have dampers to control the burning rate.

I am not aware that any tests have been done on these units but it is safe to say that they certainly increase the efficiency of the fire. If fitted with doors, circulating fireplaces have the potential for reaching efficiencies as high as wood stoves. The addition of doors will also cut down on uncomfortable draughts. An added refinement is to feed air to the fire from outside the house. This will be a further help in cutting down draughts. It could be difficult retrofitting an existing house with outside ducts but if building a new house it is worth remembering this point.

Woodstoves

Assuming one wants a woodstove, and not a multi-fuel central heating unit, then there are three basic types to choose from:
1. Space heating stoves
2. Heating stoves with back boiler for domestic water heating
3. Cookstoves

Space heating stoves are the most straightforward and come in all shapes and sizes. Installation in, or in front of, an existing fireplace poses no problems. Most, but not all, stoves have one or two hot plates on top for cooking.

A good stove will boil a kettle within ten minutes of lighting the stove. By good I mean an air-tight stove which draws all air for the fire through the draft control which is usually set in the front firedoor.

How Stoves Work

A central heating panel heats by convection, air comes into contact with the panel, is heated and in rising circulates. An open fire heats mainly by radiation, that is the rays of the fire heat the body much like the sun. The difference between radiation and convection is that radiant heat travels at the speed of light and gives a greater feeling of warmth than convection which travels slower and tends to give a more general background heat. Heat coming from woodstoves is a mixture of the two but more heat is transferred by radiation than convection. The ratio depends upon the surface heat of the stove but at 100°F the convection to radiation ratio is 1:2 and at 750°F is 1:3.

So, with stoves one benefits from immediate radiant heat after ten minutes or so for the fire to get going. Later the background room temperature is raised by convection.

Convection or circulating stoves give — as their name implies — most of their heat in the form of convection. This is achieved by using a second outer skin around the stove with air vents at the bottom and top through which air circulates and is heated before being returned to the room. While convection stoves still give off a proportion of their heat as radiation, they are generally regarded as being safer — especially where children are around — as the surface temperature is less than with ordinary stoves.

The Jotul No. 6 which can be used as either an open or closed wood-stove.

Efficiency

The reason why an open fireplace is so inefficient is because there is no draught controller to regulate the incoming air hence the rate at which the wood burns is almost impossible to control. Most of the heat from the fire leaves quickly via the chimney, particularly if the chimney is set against an outside wall.

Woodstoves differ in that the volume of air required for combustion can be closely governed by the draught and damper controls. Therefore the chilly draught associated with open fires is avoided. Most of the air drawn by the open hearth is unnecessary for combustion.

Baffles are arranged inside most stoves and these cause the exit of the hot flue gases to be delayed by forcing them

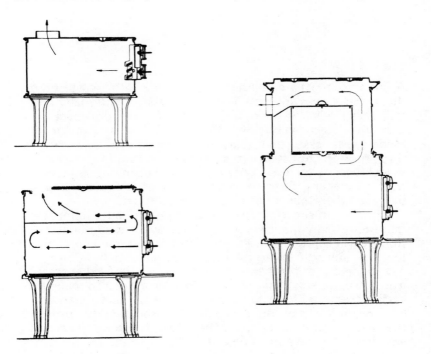

Three stoves from the Lange range illustrate the use of smoke circulating baffles. 1) Plain Stove 2) Stove with baffle 3) Stove with arch.

through an S-bend. The longer the gases remain in the stove the greater the output. An advance on this principle is the use of a heat circulating arch.

The average efficiency of most stoves is about 50% rising to 60% or 70% with a good baffle system.

Chimney heat extractors are available as stove accessories. These can be active systems driven by a fan or passive systems using convection. Whichever type it is, it basically consists of a flue or chimney attachment heated by the flue smoke and then giving up its heat to the room. Heat extractors can increase the efficiency of the woodstove installation by about 5%.

Steel or Iron?

A fair amount of argument goes on as to whether cast iron or sheet steel stoves are best. The truth is that functionally both materials are just as good, but each has its own drawback — light sheet steel can buckle if the fire is burnt too hot for too long whereas cast iron can crack if dropped or if cold water is thrown on the hot stove. It is advisable to avoid light gauge sheet stoves as they will only buckle and burn out. ¼ inch steel is excellent, three sixteenth of an inch is fine but anything less than that is unsuitable in most cases.

Another aspect to watch out for is poor quality in manufacture. A badly made stove should be avoided at all costs since it will smoke the user out of house and home, and by the time you go back to the manufacturer he will probably have gone out of business. I have never heard of a dye cast iron stove, unless it was an old secondhand one. To make the castings required for a new iron stove costs a fortune and so before going into production manufacturers tend to ensure that the end product deserves the effort. Nor have I heard of any cast iron stove burning out and so I think we can be fairly confident that quality cast iron stoves do not burn out under normal woodburning use.

To illustrate my point about the futility of buying a light gauge sheet steel stove I will recount what happened with one such stove called the 'Tinlizze' made from one sixteenth of an inch steel and now fortunately, out of production. Not only was the stove made of light sheet steel but it was also bolted rather than welded together. The result was that when the fire got going it let air in through all its joints and the fire was very difficult to control. Worse still the Tinlizze often leaked smoke into the room, particularly when the draught was poor just after the fire had been lit. If used for any length of time the walls of this particular stove would begin to buckle thus increasing the size of the gaps between the joints and making an already smokey stove even worse. I have not heard of anyone who persisted in using a Tinlizze for very long but I am sure that it would not take more than a few years to burn out a one sixteenth of an inch steel stove. And even with a double skin, a burnt out stove is still a very dangerous animal. As I say the Tinlizze is now out of production but do watch out for, and avoid, any you see for sale secondhand.

The above example is not an indictment against all steel stoves. Take for example, the well made Quebb which is an

The Quebb
made from ¼inch boiler plate steel

airtight stove made from ¼ inch boiler plate steel which has internal baffles on the walls to protect them even further. The Quebb is welded and not bolted together and this is what gives it its airtight quality. It is regrettable that rubbish such as the Tinlizze should tarnish other products which are perfectly good.

I have said that for the purposes of heating and combustion there is no real difference between a good steel or iron stove of the same gauge. The radiant heat of a heavy cast iron stove tends to be steadier and 'feel' better than a lighter steel stove, but if they are of the same gauge I can't see that there would be any difference in performance. There is an aesthetic difference in that it is possible to cast motifs and decorative symbols on iron stoves whereas it is not so easy to beautify steel stoves. An example of this is the beautiful motif on the side of the Jotul cast iron stove no. 118.

Note the motif on the side of the Jotul 118.

Hot Water

Many stoves are available with back boilers as an optional extra. Back boilers can be connected directly or indirectly to the domestic hot water tank. With the direct or open system hot water is fed directly into the tank, with the indirect or closed system a heat exchanger in the tank is used. The same principles are used with solar panels. The difference between solar and wood heating is that wood can heat all year round although you need to constantly fuel the fire, whereas the solar panel only heats really effectively in summer but once it is installed it needs little further attention.

Output from a back boiler is directly related to the state of the fire. Maximum output tends to be from about one kilowatt upwards. With a good fire I have had the hot water tank reach boiling point on many occasions, particularly on

Ulefos 865 woodstove cut away to show back boiler.

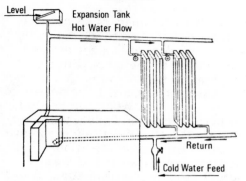

RADIATORS

Level

Expansion Tank

Hot Water Flow

Return

Cold Water Feed

Note: Base of radiators must be above
level of return to boiler

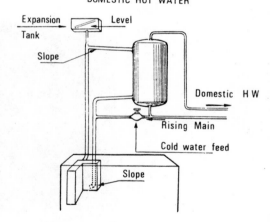

DOMESTIC HOT WATER

Expansion
Tank

Level

Slope

Domestic H W

Rising Main

Cold water feed

Slope

*Plumbing arrangements for the provision of central heating and domestic
hot water from certain woodstoves and multi-fuel burners.*

bath nights. With back boilers do make sure than an overflow vent is installed leading to the top-up tank or outside the house. In addition a pressure release valve is a useful precaution. The output from some back boilers can supply heat to a radiator panel or two in addition to tap water but it needs a fair sized stove to do this.

Cookstoves

Wood-fired cookstoves usually come with back boilers and many of them have sufficient output to heat not just the tap water but also a number of central heating radiators. As they can combine three functions in one, wood-fired cookstoves are coming back into vogue again and this is despite the ease of electric cooking. In America cookstoves fired by wood are very popular, some people swear by the 'flavoursome cooking' they give. And if you have the wood why not use it, though there is an art and a knack to successful woodstove cookery. Some stoves like the Jotul 118 can be used to smoke fish. The best wood to use is oak and three to seven hours smoking should yield tasty results.

Fosse Warmair's imported Deville C44 cookstoves with boiler for hot water and central heating.

The Stanley woodburning cooker.

Lighting a Stove

If you don't want to use firelighters for the rest of your days the following is a quick and easy method. Roll up single sheets of newspaper into long rolls, tie or fold each one up into a loose knot and put three to five of these on the ashbed. Put some small pieces of dry kindling on top, add a few sticks, put a match to the paper, close the fire door, open the draught controller and the result should be a good fire. It helps to develop a good fire if two splits of wood are put at either side of the stove with the paper and kindling in between.

If the fire does not light up well it may be that the flue or chimney is not drawing enough because it is cold. The way around this is to stuff some newspaper in the flue at the back of the stove, light the paper and the resulting blaze should get a good draught in the right direction.

Firebox Control

There are two mechanisms for controlling the rate of wood burning in a stove, first the draught regulator, of which there can be one or two, usually set in the stove door, and second the damper in the flue at the back of the stove — stove dampers are usually butterfly valves. The draught controls the flow of air to the fire and the damper produces the same effect by decreasing the smoke vent size. Combustion is more complete when the draught is left open and the damper closed down (but not shut). When the draught regulator is closed and the damper is open the fire smokes without flames. Much of the heat escapes as dense smoke which is obviously a waste. If you want to dampen a blazing fire quickly add some wet or green wood and use the controls to the maximum. Thick magazines can also smother or dampen a fire as they don't burn.

Overnight Burning

A sure sign of a good stove is one which will keep a fire going overnight. The idea is that the airtight stove smoulders overnight with the controls closed down and then when the draught is opened in the morning, the fire leaps into flames and is just right for fuelling with fresh firewood. To keep a fire in overnight what is required in the evening is a bed of glowing wood coals or embers on top of which is laid hardwood 'in the round', smaller logs at the bottom and larger at the top, they need not be air-dry. Hardwood burns slower than softwood and the round logs help the fire stay in longer. That way the stove should stay in overnight and give out a steady background heat.

Overnight fires tend to smoke and so deposit tar and creosote in the flue. To burn this off let the fire blaze in the morning for 20 minutes or for an hour once a week.

Stove Output

Assessing stove output is not as easy as it is with an electric appliance. A single bar electric fire uses one kilowatt (kW) and if it is on for an hour the power consumed and the heat given is one kilowatt hour (kWh), which in turn equals 3413 British thermal units (Btu). By its very nature a stove does not have such precisely determined output levels.

The heat value to be gained from any stove is limited by the firebox capacity, the stove surface area, the amount of wood put into it and the rate of burning. Most manufacturers state in kWh or Btu terms the maximum output of their stoves. Heat requirement calculations should be based on average stove output and not on the maximum which is only achieved with the stove going full blast.

If your current heating system is electric then finding out your heat requirements is easy, just find out the rating of each appliance, add up the number of hours each is on and that will give a clear idea of what you need. The same can be said for gas and oil central heating systems. But anyone with a central heating system will probably have calculated their heat requirements by following the standard procedure for heat loss measurement. Leaflets clearly explaining such procedure are freely available from any central heating contractor, and there is little point in reprinting the details here.

To cut down on central heating bills a stove can be installed in the hall and while some of the heat will go to the downstairs rooms, most of it will be convected upstairs. Alternatively the stove, or a second one, can be placed in the main living room which will also help to heat the house and particularly the room upstairs. A cookstove in the kitchen will also contribute some background heat in the house and keep the kitchen good and warm.

Some manufacturers state their stove outputs in terms of

heating so many square or cubic feet. This is a far from satis-factory system as the variations from house to house are extreme when it comes to heating. A well insulated house with average window space will only require half the Btu's that an uninsulated house of the same size with a lot of glass in it would require. Another factor which is not always in-cluded in such area estimates is the relative outside and inside temperatures. So, base your calculations not upon the 'space' a stove can heat but rather on its rated kW or Btu output, and remember that the maximum output is the maximum and not the likely actual output.

Multi-Fuel Boilers

To maintain a basic level of comfort in a small cottage only one or, at the most, two woodstoves would be required. If the intention is to use wood or other biofuels to heat a country house then a multi-fuel boiler is probably ideal for central heating and hot water supply. Multi-fuel boilers, or burners and furnaces as they are also called, may be used to heat ordinary wet radiator panels or to supply hot air to ducted systems. Many householders, mainly farmers and those who own woodlots, are now saving a lot of money by burning locally available fuel. Only a few years ago multi-fuel burners were virtually unheard of in the UK although some manufacturers on the continent have been producing them for years. There are now eight makes available and with a particularly good economic argument going for them sales are booming.

Multi-fuel burners will, as their name implies, burn just about any type of fuel: oil, gas, coal, peat, wood, straw and even rubbish, though plastic is to be avoided. I know of one baker who partially fuelled his boiler with stale bread. Another case is of a joinery factory which once paid to get rid of its waste (sawdust etc.) and now burns it to heat the factory. Similar stories abound among multi-fuel burner dealers. Basically anything that is combustible and reasonably dry will burn, even the 'rag trade' can benefit by burning waste material.

Farmers, in particular, are interested in the use of multi-fuel burners seeing in them a cheaper way to heat their

The multi-fuel furnace will take bales of straw and even 3ft logs.

homes and outhouses, also for such purposes as grain drying. The heat output of a bale of straw equals about 1.2 gallons of oil. At 38p a gallon that gives an equivalent value of 46p a bale. If straw costs 10p a bale into the bargain it then follows that a considerable saving can be made. So, instead of burning straw in the field why not harvest it as a fuel crop? As a matter of interest, farmers who rotate their corn crops with oil seed rape have a good source of fuel in the rape straw.

Multi-fuel burners are essentially just big woodstoves with

The Franco Belge multi-fuel cooker/boiler which heats up to 15 radiators.

the added advantage of fuel adaptability. The best place to put the burner is in an outhouse or basement. Existing conventionally fuelled boilers can easily be adapted to a solid fuel multi-burner. With such combinations one then has the economy of cheap solid fuel and the convenience of conventional fuel should solid fuel supplies run out. It is also possible to time the oil or gas burner to heat the house in the early morning before the first solid fuelling takes place. Many manufacturers supply optional gas/oil/electricity burners or elements which can be used in or with the solid fuel multi-burner. For example, Passat supply a small oil-fired unit which sits on top of their solid fuel multi-burner. A thermostatic control can automatically switch on in the oil unit if the output from the solid fuel burner is insufficient.

By their very nature multi-burners use more fuel than woodstoves. To be precise about requirements is difficult as the figures vary from house to house. Suffice to say that a fair sized house with reasonable insulation would require about 6 to 8 cords of wood or 1,000 bales of straw a year to supply central heating and hot water. On the other hand, a typical uninsulated farmhouse would require more fuel.

A cord of wood occupies an area of 4 x 4 x 8 ft., therefore six cords takes up about 750 cubic feet. It is best to keep wood left outside under the cover of plastic sheeting. A month's supply at a time can then be brought into the boiler room which helps to dry the wood before burning. Most multi-fuel burners take logs up to 3ft long and as such the burner only needs fuelling twice a day. If bales of straw are used the fuelling is more frequent, about four times a day.

Multi-fuel boilers have thermostatically controlled draught regulators which closely govern the combustion rate and this is what prevents a bale of straw from burning out in a few minutes. Most multi-burners have additional draught inlets which let in sufficient oxygen to mix with the hot gases and thus cause a secondary combustion. Gas combustion increases the efficiency of the unit. Cleaning is only required once or twice weekly with wood as it burns well on a good ashbed.

Calorific Value of Fuels per lb.

Fuel oil	18,300 Btu approx.
House Coal	13,500 Btu approx.
Turf	6,000 Btu approx.
Briquettes	8,000 Btu approx.
Wood (air dry)	6,500 Btu approx.
Straw (wheat)	7,600 Btu approx.
Newspapers/magazines (dry)	7,000 Btu approx.
Sawdust	7,000 Btu approx.

WARNING — Sawdust

The use of sawdust as a fuel in multi-burners or woodstoves is to be avoided unless a special automatic stoker is used to turn the sawdust and mix the gases with oxygen. If burnt without a stoker, first it will be difficult to get a fire going, but more important, there may result a dangerous build-up of gas which could cause an explosion.

The exception to this is the Fulgora stove which is intended to burn sawdust.

Chimneys and Stove Location

The Siting

The siting of a stove or multi-burner and its correct installation are just as important as the choice of stove itself. Most house fires associated with the use of stoves are a result of improper installation. By following correct procedure with regard to distancing the stove and flue away from combustible materials, the risk of fire is rendered negligible. Smoking stoves can generally be corrected by improving the flue pipe arrangement.

Stove Location

The location of a stove is obviously decided by the room or area to be heated. If the requirement is for general background heating then a central position in the hall is probably best but most of the heat will convect upstairs, that is assuming it is a two storey house.

However, it is more usual that a stove is required to heat a specific room. If there is a fireplace then the stove can stand in front of it, or if it is an inglenook then the stove can be put in it. The drawback in placing a stove inside a fireplace is that a proportion of the heat is lost to the walls, the heat loss is greater if the chimney is on an outside wall.

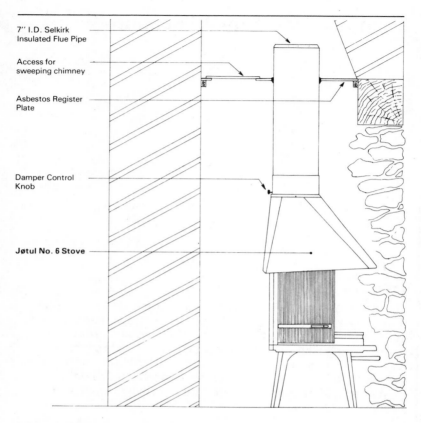

7" I.D. Selkirk
Insulated Flue Pipe

Access for
sweeping chimney

Asbestos Register
Plate

Damper Control
Knob

Jøtul No. 6 Stove

Jotul No. 6 fitted in Inglenook.

The best way to arrange a stove is to have it standing out
from the wall. This way there is a gain from both convected
and radiant heat. If you are not careful in choosing the right
stove this arrangement can look awkward, particularly with a
big stove in a small room where the stove can get in the way.
So, before parting with your money ensure that the stove
dimensions suit the room in question. At the same time
ensure that the stove outlet is no higher than the crest of the
fireplace.

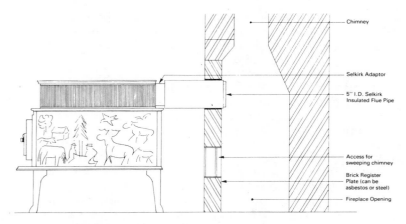

Chimney

Selkirk Adaptor

5″ I.D. Selkirk
Insulated Flue Pipe

Access for
sweeping chimney

Brick Register
Plate (can be
asbestos or steel)

Fireplace Opening

Jotul No. 118 fitted in front of a fireplace.

The heat output of stoves invariably fluctuates as the wood goes through its various stages of combustion. It is worth mentioning that some people used to thermostatically controlled central heating find this slight variation in heat not exactly to their liking. Fortunately, such people are few and far between and anyway the variations are usually far less than with an ordinary coal fire. Putting the stove inside an inglenook or fireplace will balance the heat as the mass of stone absorbs much of the heat before re-radiating it at a more constant temperature. But remember that this way it will take longer for the room to heat up.

The best place to site a multi-burner is in an outhouse or basement and if there is space in the same room to store wood, even better. If there is no suitable room or outhouse then you will have to add an extension to the house. To place a woodstove in a basement with the intention of gaining general background heat in the house is a waste of time as most of the heat is lost through the walls and floor.

Stove Clearance

Intense radiant heat from stoves, multi-burners, flues and chimneys can cause the combustion of any other inflammable material (including plasterboard) which comes into contact with the hot surface.

Stoves should be kept three feet away from unprotected walls and furniture and one foot away if the surface is protected by sheet steel or asbestos. An air gap should be left between the steel and the surface as the sheet itself can get hot enough to cause a fire. I know of a case in point where a wooden wall next to a stove was protected by a steel plate without any gap between the metal and the wood. When the danger of this was pointed out and the metal removed the wood was found to be charred. It is best to have the stove legs six inches away from a wooden floor. Stone or brick stove platforms should be built on a sheet steel base as stone itself does not necessarily protect combustibles. The importance of ensuring correct stove clearance cannot be overstressed.

When installing a stove in an open fireplace use a sheet steel or asbestos register plate to block off the chimney or fireplace and render it airtight with firebrick cement. Cut a hole in the plate to take the section of flue pipe from the stove into the chimney. An access to facilitate chimney cleaning should also be made.

If you are one of those unfortunate few who have bought a house without a chimney you can install a flue pipe or a fabricated chimney. If taking a flue through the roof ensure that the required clearances are strictly adhered to.

Flue Pipe and Prefabricated Chimneys

The best type of flue is the insulated double walled type. There are various makes available such as Selkirk Metalbestos (doesn't contain asbestos), Parakaflue and Enviromark Twin Walled Pipe, all are available from local stockists of heating equipment. An insulated flue has an advantage in that it heats up quickly and so enhances draught and inhibits creosote deposits. Insulated pipe is safer and requires less clearance space between it and combustibles.

An internal chimney flue. Correct stovepipe clearances are essential.

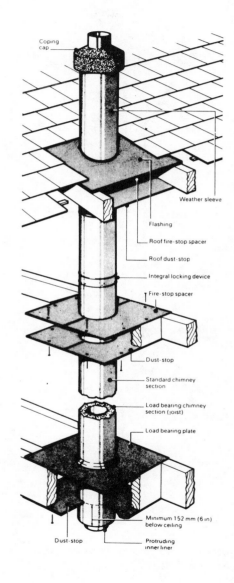

Coping cap

Weather sleeve

Flashing

Roof fire-stop spacer

Roof dust-stop

Integral locking device

Fire-stop spacer

Dust-stop

Standard chimney section

Load bearing chimney section (joist)

Load bearing plate

Minimum 152 mm (6 in) below ceiling

Dust-stop

Protruding inner liner

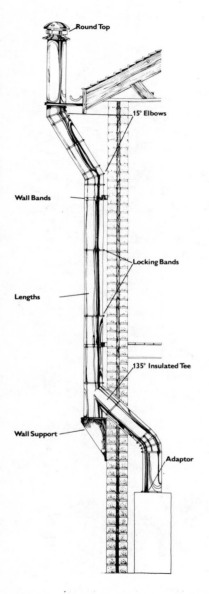

Round Top

15° Elbows

Wall Bands

Locking Bands

Lengths

135° Insulated Tee

Wall Support

Adaptor

Outside chimneys tend to lose more heat than internal ones but are easier to install.

The cheapest type of flue is plain single walled steel pipe which is definitely not recommended for home use. The wall inevitably corrodes and releases creosote which deposits on the outside where it can easily catch fire. Steel pipe can have a life of less than five years and so there is really little point in using such material especially since proper pipe can be bought for little extra in cost.

Whatever flue pipe you use be sure it is suitable for use with wood stoves, some pipe intended for gas burners is definitely not suitable.

The only place I would use a single walled flue is if it is intended to go just from the stove to a few inches on the other side of the register plate. Even so I would use cast iron and not steel pipe.

When erecting flue pipes be sure to fit the joints with the female end upwards otherwise there will be difficulty with creosote and condensation leaking to the outside of the pipes and becoming a potential fire risk.

Thermoflue Ltd. manufacture insulated chimney units which have integral flue liners. These block-like units are cemented together to give a solid freestanding chimney very useful if that is what you want. Sections of insulated pipes screw into each other but they, on the other hand, require support.

How a Flue Functions

Without a flue pipe the smoke in the stove would not be able to differentiate between the door, draught regulator and the flue exit — even an outdoor barbecue stove requires a length of pipe. The purpose of stove pipe is to create up-draught, suction or pull which results from a combination of the height of the flue and the temperature difference between flue gases and outside air. Basically the smoke in the flue is hotter than the air and therefore the smoke rises. The warmer and taller the flue the better the draught and without draught the fire will not start or at its best be sluggish.

Sharp bends or steep angles in a flue cause resistance to the flow of smoke and should be eliminated as far as possible, particularly in the case of open fires. Air leaking into the flue has the effect of cooling the smoke and so inhibiting the draught. Small joint leaks in a flue pipe with good draught will generally have no negative effect on stove performance.

A difficulty can arise with too much draught, particularly when the stove is set to burn slowly and too much 'draw' causes overheating. The sure remedy for this, to be used after the damper and draught regulators have been played to the full, is to fit an adjustable draught stabiliser which will draw additional air into the flue and so reduce the draught. This results in a steady burning rate.

The most frequent cause of smoking chimneys is the wind acting on the flue top. Obviously if the wind is blowing directly into the chimney there will be trouble at the other end. But what is not so obvious is the effect that roof-tops or trees have in causing wind turbulance which leads to downdraughts. This is why it is always recommended that a chimney be at least 3 ft higher than any object within a 10ft radius. If the downdraught still continues after this standard has been met then increase the height so that the outlet is higher than anything within a 20 — 30 ft radius. An alternative to this is to fit a chimney-cap which is frequently a very effective way to cure downdraught problems. Rotating chimney-caps are not a good idea for use with woodstoves as they tend to foul up with tar and creosote. A flat stone or tile on four pillars is the cheapest and most common cap used on brickwork chimneys and a whole variety of metal ones are available from hardware shops for stove pipe.

Smoking stoves can be caused by a house that is too well insulated. If insufficient air is admitted to the house then there will be a difficulty with combustion which will result in a poor fire and can cause downdraughts. Fortunately there are very few houses so well insulated as to cause this problem, particularly with closed stoves as they only require from 30 — 60 cubic feet of air a minute. Open fireplaces are a different matter as they require from 100 — 300 cubic feet a minute which may be difficult to obtain in a well insulated house.

What generally happens in these cases of 'air starvation' is that the fire will just burn badly, downdraughts rarely occur with closed stoves but can happen with open fireplaces. The cure for this trouble usually depends on opening a window or ducting air under the floor directly to the burner.

There is another reason for downdraughts which has nothing to do with insulation. When warm air inside the house itself is acting as draught by rising to the top of the house, this causes chimney downdraught as fresh air is drawn in to replace the rising warm air. This usually occurs with two storey and not single storey houses, and is called the stack effect. It is most noticeable in tall buildings with central heating where a severe draught can be experienced when opening the front ground floor doors. To avoid this problem put some paper into the chimney connector and light it. The burning paper will get the draught flowing up the flue and especially so if insulated flue is used. If the stove is lit when this admittedly rare down-draught does occur then there is little that can be done except open a downstairs window.

Chimneys and prefabricated flue pipes should be cleaned regularly, at least once a year. This is particularly important if burning damp or green wood as it tends to cause considerable creosote deposits. Chemical cleaners which cause the creosote to peel off may be used but even so it is best to brush down the stack with a chimney brush or to employ the services of your local chimney sweep. Regular cleaning will prevent chimney fires which can be devastating and frightening. Whatever else be sure to clean the chimney before installing a stove.

Safety

A woodstove or multi-fuel burner will cause no danger or problem if properly installed and if the chimney is cleaned regularly. If the chimney is not cleaned then it is only a matter of time before creosote deposits catch fire, an occurrence which can be particularly disastrous if a single walled flue pipe is used. Apart from that the following points should be noted:

1. Make sure that the burner is installed strictly according to the manufacturer's instructions and kept well away from any combustible material.
2. Keep furniture, newspapers, toys etc., 4 ft or more away from the stove.
3. Burn stove hot for 20 or 30 minutes after any slow-burning period, for example overnight burning, or when quantities of green wood have been burnt. This action helps to burn off creosote deposits.
4. Invest in a fire extinguisher.
5. Examine the stove periodically for signs of deterioration.

Back-puffing

Back-puffing is an unusual but unpleasant occurrence which is worth taking steps to avoid. It can happen with a stove where the draught regulator is shut down and the fuelling door is suddenly opened causing smoke to be drawn back into the firebox where it mixes with incoming air and flames from the wood, the result of which can be a minor explosion as secondary combustion of the smoke takes place.

As I say, this is a rare event and constitutes no real danger The only difficulty that can arise is if the owner of the stove decides to stick his head in the firebox door to see what is happening. So the idea is not to lean forward when opening the stove door. It is also a good idea to open the draught regulator fully for a minute or two before fuelling the stove or boiler as this helps to clear the air inside the firebox.

Fuel for the Fire

'Old wood is best to burn old wine to drink and old friends
to trust'

Francis Bacon

In rural areas there is an abundance of wood fuel just waiting
to be burnt. An average sized insulated house would require
only about two tons of wood a year to fuel a woodstove.
Estimates have been made that there is *at least one million
tons of wood fuel available in the UK annually.* This figure
does not include wood taken for other uses in the timber
trade, nor does it include the regrettable amount of dead Elm
littering the country-side — reckoned to be about 11.5
million trees with each tree weighing about a ton. The waste
left over from timber imports is another useful source. All
in all there is ample fuel to fire many more woodstoves and
multi-burners.

Assessing Firewood Availability

The thing to do before buying a wood-burning appliance is to
ensure that an adequate supply of fuel is available. The fortunate few who own a few acres of woodland have no problem
other than maintaining the trees and harvesting the annual
yield. Woodlot development is covered in the next chapter.
If you do not own woodland then make the best of British
forests. The Forestry Commission is sometimes open to arrangements whereby local people can have the 'lop and top',

the waste, in exchange for removing it. If you live near the forest and are handy with a chain saw then it is well worth approaching the caretaker to see if some arrangement can be agreed upon. The 'waste' from coniferous woodland is far less than from deciduous, the first have very small branches compered to the broadleaves.

Living elms are known for their tendency to drop a branch without notice, regrettable if it falls on the head of an unwary passer-by. Dead elms are even more notorious in this respect and as such they are being cut down in their millions but once down the wood has to be removed. Due to a glut of elm at most sawmills the wood is now frequently burnt where it falls. This excellent source of free fuel should be better used. Contractors who fell and cut the tree can sometimes be paid to deliver it to your home. Alternatively you can tackle the felled tree yourself with a chain saw. It certainly makes more sense to burn it in a stove or multi-burner rather than leave it to rot or burn it in the field.

Tree cutters, surgeons and those who prune and thin trees in town and country are paid not just to cut but also to remove the cuttings. Ask any of them what they do with it and you will find that it usually gets burnt in the open. Tip them a few pounds and fill your backyard with wood ready for seasoning. Watch out that you don't get a truck load of twigs.

Over much of the countryside there abounds quantities of waste wood passed by unnoticed by all except the woodstove user who quickly develops an eye for free fuel. Nearly all farms have trees which can be pruned or else cut down and replaced with saplings. Hedgerows are another source of useful firewood. And, of course, the farmer can always bale and burn his own straw in a multi-burner.

The urban dweller has a much more difficult task when it comes to gathering wood fuel. The best sources are furniture manufacturers, timber yards, demolition sites and, for the really determined, refuse dumps. Manufacturers and timber yards usually have a constant source of waste which they like to dispose of regularly. Therefore it is best to come to some collection arrangement which suits the supplier even if this means you will have a build-up of wood during the summer. Teams of men armed with chain saws can often be seen pruning urban trees and they are happy to take care of the waste.

Buying Wood

Having exhausted free or almost free sources of wood the next place to try is a timber yard where wood can be bought at an economic cost of £10 or £12 a ton. Those who do not want to get involved with chain saws and log splitting may choose to buy from a wood merchant from the start. The two standard measures for wood is the cord and the ton. The cord is equal to approximately 80 cu. ft of solid wood which when stacked takes up an area of 4 ft wide by 4 ft high by 8 ft long, 128 cu ft in all which is reduced to 80 cu ft when the air space between the logs is deducted.

A ton of wood is a dubious measure as the wood can be green and so have a high moisture content which adds weight, hence one would be buying a mixture of wood and water. There is little point in paying good money for water. Left for a summer in the sun the original ton can be reduced in weight considerably. So, if the wood merchant is selling by the ton instead of by the cord, or some similar measure, ask him if the wood has been seasoned (air-dried to a moisture content of about 20%) or not. If not or if the wood looks wet and grotty then bargain with him to reduce the price.

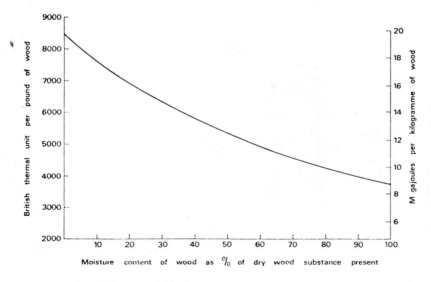

Useful heat available from wood at different moisture contents

If selling by bulk instead of weight then the price does not matter, as long as it is a reasonble one. What does matter however is whether the wood is suitable for burning or not. If air dried, that is out in the open for the summer preferably a year, then it is fit for the fire and will yield between 6,000 and 6,500 Btu's per pound. But if it is greenwood, wet and damp, with a high moisture content, then the useful heat output can be reduced to less than 4,000 Btu's. Moreover greenwood causes tar and condensation problems in the chimney. So, where possible season the wood before burning.

Felling trees

Apart from swinging an axe, the only quick way to fell timber is with the use of a chainsaw, or pay someone else to use one. There can be no denying that chainsaws are noisy, smelly and dangerous. Working with one is far from pleasant. Yet they do make very quick work of felling and logging.

There are a good number of chainsaws available in the UK and competition keeps the prices low but still it is worthwhile shopping around for the one which feels best at the

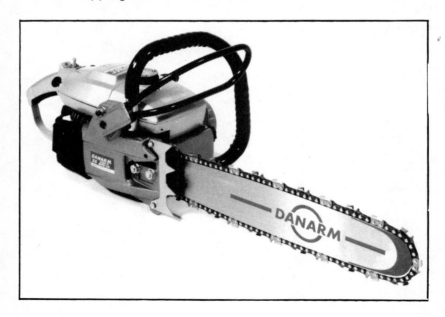

right price. Saws with 12 inch chains cost about £90 and with 16 inch chains £160. Electric saws with 10 inch chains can be bought for about £50. Secondhand saws are often not in very good condition. Hire shops rent them for between £5 and £10 a day. The reason why the rate is so high is because most people don't know how to use them and so the saw ends up damaged. If you intend cutting on a regular basis it probably works out cheaper to buy your own. Those who want to cut more than two or three cords a year should buy the heaviest saw they can handle because the smaller ones may burn out due to overuse.

Most chainsaws are imported, except for the Danarm. The size of saw chosen is determined by the width of the trees to be felled. For example, a saw with a 10 inch blade is only good for felling trees with trunks up to 18 inch or so in width. If you have never felled timber before or used a chainsaw it is advisable to choose a saw with a 16 inch or smaller blade. Electric chainsaws are far quicker and lighter but are only good for home logging as opposed to woodland working.

The use of protective clothing is an important safety factor. First and foremost wear lightweight clothing to allow full freedom of movement. Keep your jacket buttoned or zipped and do not have a scarf hanging loose. Heavy protective gloves will save your hands from a lot of scratches and cuts. Good boots or heavy shoes will help you to stand firmly and will protect your feet. Earmuffs or earplugs will make the job less unpleasant. And finally, when felling, wear a helmet. By following closely the manufacturer's chainsaw operation instructions and wearing the proper clothing, the danger is reduced considerably.

Before felling, check that there are no obstacles within range of the tree such as electricity or phone lines. If there are it would be best to call in an expert. Next take a good look at the tree and judge the direction in which it leans as that is the way it will fall. It is difficult to fell a tree against the direction of lean.

That decided, the next step is to cut a wedge shaped notch (just like a wedge of cheese) in the trunk which will allow the tree to fall in the right direction. So if the tree is to fall to the north the wedge is to be cut out of the north side of the trunk. It is not essential but is best to have the top line of the notch at 45° and the bottom line on the horizontal. The notch should be about one third or one quarter of the tree's diameter.

Having cut and removed the wedge then start the felling cut at the opposite side of the tree. Begin the cut slightly above the angle of the notch and work slowly inwards keeping the guide bar parallel to the notch. Never saw all the way through the tree but leave a break-off section of an inch or so which acts as a hinge and guides the tree as it falls. Lift the saw out and move away quickly as the tree begins to fall. The end of the tree may kick up or rear back as the tree falls.

Felling trees of a diameter greater than the saw or 'guide bar' length requires more thought. The same wedge is cut. Next a stab cut is made parallel to the notch cut but about an inch above it; leave another inch gap between the stab cut and the wedge. This second gap provides the break-off hinge section to guide the tree in its fall. For example, if you are using a 12 inch saw on a 22 inch tree, the stab cut should extend into the tree for 11 or 12 inches. The stab cut is then continued by sawing round the tree with the tip staying in the same place and the operator moving around the tree. Be careful not to cut into the break-off hinge. When making the stab cut be sure that the saw is running at top speed when you insert the tip and saw with the underside of the tip for the first inch or so before levelling out otherwise the risk of kick-back with stab cuts becomes very high. Chainsaw kick-back is nasty and can be dangerous.

Felling wedges are required when cutting trees that are wider than the saw or guide bar length. You can make your own simply by cutting a thin wedge of wood or you can buy plastic ones. Whatever you do, do not use metal wedges. The wedges are inserted in the cut as you move around the tree. If there is difficulty in getting the tree to fall the wedges can be hammered in to give a push.

Sometimes trees which are felled get hung up on adjacent trees. This is a difficulty which deserves to be approached with caution. If the tree is not too tightly stuck then make a stab cut straight through the trunk about a foot or so up from the original cut. Insert a crowbar or a branch through the cut. Next saw through the break-off hinge but leave an inch at the end to hold the tree on to the stump. Using the crow-bar lever try to roll the tree free. Be sure to roll it away from your body and be ready to move out of the way quickly if the tree does come free. If the tree remains hung-up get a good length of rope, tie one end to the tree, then use a tractor or Land Rover to haul it free. If the area is inaccessible, call in your friends together with any horses, mules or oxen you can muster up and get them all hauling on the rope while keeping a respectful distance away from the trees.

Logging Fuelwood

Having felled the tree the next job is limbing - cutting off
the branches. A quick swing with an axe will remove many
of the smaller branches with less noise and greater ease than
the saw will. With bigger branches try to stand on the opposite side of the tree and resting the saw engine on the tree,
work through the branch. Mind your feet as the branch
falls.

When cutting the trunk or large branches see which way
the tree is held in tension. Cut from below if the tree is suspended like a bridge and cut from above if it hangs forward
like an aeroplane wing.

At this stage you can cut the wood into lengths suitable
for burning, for example 3 ft for multi-fuel burners and 1.5 ft
or so for stoves, alternatively it can be cut into cord lengths
of 4 ft. If the main tree trunk is straight and true you may
choose to sell it as lumber to a sawmill in which case ask the
sawmill what lengths they want it in. The rest of the wood
can then be carted home in a truck or tractor and used for
fuel.

Once home the wood should be stacked and allowed to
dry for a year or at least six months. The general pattern is to
fell trees or buy in green wood in the autumn and store it
for use the following winter by which time it is good and dry.
Cutting deciduous trees when in leaf is messy as the leaves
get in the way and if you are felling it is difficult to see which
direction the tree is likely to fall.

Before burning them some of the logs will have to be split
or cut in half. The easiest way to cut logs in half is to put
them in a crib or hold them firmly between four stakes and
then go through the lot, right down the middle with a chain
saw.

For splitting logs you will need a good splitting maul. An
axe is only useful for the light work. A maul has a thick
blunt edge that does not get as firmly embedded in the
wood as an axe does with its thin blade. If a couple of swings
with a maul does not split the log then insert a splitting
wedge (usually steel) and hammer it home with the back of
the maul.

A handy carrier for taking fuel from the woodpile into the
house can be made with a sheet of canvas or an ordinary
grain sack. Using rope, or whatever is handy, fix two handles,

one at each end, thus making a sling. You can make re-inforced eyes to fix the handle or stitch it into the fabric. The carrier will help make the handling of firewood much easier and will keep dirt from falling on the floor.

Various wood holders can be made or bought for keeping a stock of logs ready by the fire. The design chosen, whether it be round or rectangular, can complement the shape of the stove and so create a very pleasant effect in the room. If you know of a local blacksmith, and they are not all that rare even these days, he could probably knock one up to your specifications in no time at all.

Your Own Woodlot

If you burn wood why not plant trees?

The practice of buying or planting your own woodlot to ensure a steady supply of firewood is far from uncommon in the US. Indeed they are more fortunate than us in that one third of their land is wooded whereas less than 10% of ours is under wood. There is no lack of land suitable for tree planting, particularly in upland areas where the cost is around £300 a hectare (2½ acres). Lowland of poor agricultural quality can be quite cheap. On the other hand woodland with trees about 40 to 50 years old can be worth up to £4,000 a hectare.

The Forestry Commission actively assists woodland owners by helping them to bring existing woods into full production and to plant new ones. As well as providing professional and technical assistance, the Commission offers grants of up to £300 a hectare for areas of 0.25 to 3 hectares and £25 a hectare for areas of 3 — 10 hectares. This is under the Small Woods Scheme, introduced in October 1977, and is certain to be of interest to many existing and potential woodlot owners. For areas in excess of 10 hectares, grants are available under the Dedication Scheme.

The beauty of the Small Woods Scheme is that it does not distinguish between conifers and broadleaves, so the choice is open provided it fits in with the local landscape. A woodlot of 7½ acres (3 hectares) is ideal for harvesting an annual yield of firewood for a small to medium sized house which uses wood for all heating purposes. Depending on the condition of the wood the annual harvest for 7½ acre plot is between 3 and 8 tons of fuel. Should one choose to plant a larger area, say 25 acres, then the woodlot can be treated both as an investment and as a source of fuel whereby the timber is sold to a timber merchant and the 'lop and top' kept for fuel. Remember that the 'lop and top' on broadleaves is far greater than it is with conifers. As an investment wood can only increase in value, particularly since the traditional suppliers of wood, Scandinavia and Canada, are felling more than they are planting.

Apart from its value as fuel a well tended woodlot is an excellent place to be in and better still to have your house in. All manner of wildlife flourish in woodland and bring a good ecological balance back to a land denuded by an agricultural system that does little for the land but takes everything from it. By keeping a small section of your woodlot free from felling on a rotation system you will find that the wildlife, flora and fauna is maintained in a better balance than otherwise. This practice seems to create a 'safe' area. The concept of forest farming, whereby animals can graze among certain types of trees, is very well explained in a book of the same title by Douglas and Hart and published by Watkins of London.

A licence is usually required for the felling of growing trees, under the Forestry Act of 1967. But don't worry about that as any owner is allowed, under the Act, to fell up to 41 cords of wood annually for his own use. Even a very large farmhouse would find it difficult to burn its way through 41 cords a year. Of that quantity the owner may sell up to 2 cords.

Grants of up to 50% are available for the planting of shelter-belts under the Agriculture and Horticulture Capital Grant Schemes. These can supply not only shelter but also fuel. Taxation on woodland is also very favourably inclined toward the owner. Details of the tax situation and grant schemes are available in 'Advice for Woodland Owners' from the Forestry Commission whose headquarters is at 231, Corstorphine Road, Edinburgh EH12 7AT.

The Men of the Trees are an interesting group who foster the planting of trees, unfortunately they tend to occupy themselves more with preservation orders than with active planting. Their address is Crawley Down, Sussex. Details of other groups active in this area are included in 'Advice for Woodland Owners.'

Index of Manufacturers Part One — Woodstoves, Cookers and Open Fireplaces

Cost: The cost of all appliances shown below excludes VAT and delivery. Costs are shown for comparative purposes only and are correct at June 1978.

Output: Output is shown in kilowatts and is usually the maximum, to arrive at a more reasonable average reduce the figure by 25 — 40%. Where the average ouput is given by the manufacturer it is shown in brackets next to output. Output is variable and determined by the amount and type of wood used. Multi-burner output is shown in Btu's.

Log Length: Maximum log length the firebox will accommodate is shown in inches.

Dimensions: The height (H), width (W) and length (L) are shown in inches, measurements are approximate only.

INDEX OF MANUFACTURERS

The following is a comprehensive list of woodburning appliance manufacturers and principle importers. To list all the local agents for each make would only clog the book and cloud the issue. Make a short list of the appliances which suit your needs and then write to the manufacturers who will supply a list of agents if there are any.

Manufacturer/Importer	Make
Fosse Warmair	Deville
Fulgora Stoves	Fulgora
Home Stoves	Le Select
Hunter & Sons	Hunter
Interoven Ltd.,	Rais Producter
Jetmaster Fires	Jetmaster
Le Feu de Bois	various French makes
Light Air Workshop	Woodstove plans
Logfires Ltd.	Marlborough & Gloucester stoves
Modern Fires	Lange
Passat Ltd.	Passat
Peatol Stoves	Peatol
Quebb Stoves	Quebb
Smith & Wellstood Ltd.	Dragon Stove
Smockery Woodburning Centre	Morso
Philip Spencer Stoves	Sherwood Stoves
Strax Distribution	Ulefos
Ellis Sykes	Godin, Bjorno, Leda
Simon Thorpe	Jotul
U.A. Engineering	Franco Belge
Wade Lewis	Forrester
Waterford Ironfounders	Reginald, Stanley
Woodburning Stoves Co.	Coste
Yorkpark Ltd.	Trolla

Fosse Warmair
Old Farm, Norton Road, Iverley, Stourbridge, DY8 2RU
Tel: Hagley 5898

Fosse Warmair are agents for the French range of Deville wood, coal or
peat burning cookers and heaters made of cast iron and finished in white
enamel. Firebox size is adjustable to suit different fuels. Oven is surroun-
ded by burning gasses which gives even heat.

Model 7771 Room Heater
Room heater with large fire window. Cast iron firebox with stainless
steel combustion chamber. Burns wood and coal. Brown enamel.
£210. Nominal output 6.5 kW. 24" logs.

Model 7350 Room Heater
Pyrex glass door. Cast iron firebox with stainless steel combustion
chamber. Coal is recommended but can burn wood.
£136. Nominal output 3.3 kW. Brown enamel.

Deville 7350 (left) and Deville 7771 (right).

Model C12 Cooker
£248. Logs up to 13". Width 23½".

Model C32 Cooker
£298. Logs up to 17". Width 29½".

Model C42
Cooker with optional hot water and central heating boiler.
Basic cost £310, with hot water boiler £355, with hot water and central heating boiler £495. Logs up to 17". Width 33½".

Deville C42 cooker.

Fulgora Stoves Ltd
167, Battersea Rise, London SW11
Tel: 01-228 2464

The Fulgora is designed to burn sawdust, wood shavings and chips both green and dry. Made from sheet steel, finished in black, it consists of an inner removeable fuel chamber which rests on a supporting flange above the base of the outer container. The Fulgora was passed for use in smokeless zones in 1959.

Large size Fulgora
£45. Sawdust burner. H 36". Diameter 24".

Small size Fulgora
£37. Sawdust burner. H 36". Diameter 18".

Home Stoves Ltd
113, Warwick Avenue, London W9 2PP
Tel: 01-289 1667

The 'Le Select' is a British made reproduction of a French woodstove first produced in the 1880's. It is a highly decorative stove with mica windows and is available in black, jade, brown and royal blue. Cast iron.

£187. Output up to 5 kW. 18" logs. H 22", W 22", Depth 14½".

THE BRITISH MADE WOOD BURNING STOVE

Hunter & Son (Mells) Ltd
Frome, Somerset.
Tel: Mells 812545

Hunter manufacture two woodburning stoves which feature hot air circulation, glass panelled openable doors, optional back boiler and the stoves are available in a choice of four colours.

Medium Hunter
£169. Output up to 8 kW. 24" logs. H 37½", W 27½", Depth 18". Copper back boiler £69.

Large Hunter
£189. Output up to 12 kW. 24" logs. H 42", W 31", Depth 20". Copper back boiler £69.

Interoven Ltd
70/72, Fearnley Street, Watford, Herts, WD1 7DE
Tel: Watford 46761/2

Sole agents for the Rais Produkter Danish woodstoves. Interoven import three models and manufacture the other three in England. A unique feature of the Rais is its built-in log storage compartment which helps dry the fuel. Handmade from heavy steel plate and polished to give a 'gun barrel' finish. All Rais stoves can be either open or closed.

Rais Produkter Danish wood burning stove.

Rais No.1
£400. Output up to 9 kW. H 55", W 30", Depth 20". Rectangular shape.

Rais No.2
£250. Output up to 7/8 kW. H 43", W 24", Depth 20". Rectangular shape.

Rais No.3
£280. Output up to 7/8 kW. H 46", W 28", Depth 21". Half-round shape.

Rais No.4
Output up to 6 kW. Circular shape.

Rais No.5
£450. Output up to 9 kW. H 55", W 30", Depth 20". Rectangular shape
with double walls.

Rais No.6
£195. Output up to 5/6 kW. H 39", W 20", Depth 18". Rectangular
shape.

Jetmaster Fires Ltd
The Old Farmhouse, Gilbert Street, Ropley, Alresford, Hampshire
SO24 0BY
Tel: Monmouth 3083 or 4444

Jetmaster heat circulating fireplaces are an elegant solution to the waste

Universal 700
curing a smoking problem and increasing the heat output.

incurred by using open fires. The fires are suitable for burning all solid fuels, wood, coal, peat, etc.

There are four styles and each is available in a range of sizes and heating capacities. The firebox unit is of welded steel construction and is in the form of a double-skinned case through which air is circulated and heated. A concealed intake at the base of the fire draws in air which, after circulating through the casing, is discharged above the fireplace. This airstream supplements the fire's radiant heat output.

A range of back boilers is also available.

Prices for the range are from £122 to £399.

Le Feu de Bois
29, Clifden Road, Twickenham, Middx. TW1 4LU
Tel: 01-892 9985

Import a range of French stoves and cookers.

Kamina
A cast iron closed stove with enamel finish and Pyrex glass front. £230. Output up to 10 kW. H 32", W 29", Depth 15". Back boiler available.

Kaminatte
A scaled-down model of the Kamina. £210. Output up to 7 kW.

Kamina from Le Feu de Bois.

Nestor Martin Stoves

The Doric — £255. Output up to 17 kW.

The Norman — £155. Output up to 8 kW.

Supra Stove
A convector heater with side fuel loading. £115. Output up to 5½ kW.
H 26", W 21", L 26".

Supra Fireplace
Airtight fireplace with large glass door and hot air circulation system.
Comes as a kit with fireback, oak mantel, stone hearth, etc. £560.

Alsace Heater
Cast iron reproduction of a classic French stove, very finely decorated.
£250. Rectangular shape.

Rosieres Cookstoves
Details of this French range as follows:—
York cooker. £410 (with back boiler). Output up to 11½ kW. H 33½",
W 33½", L 24".
Lancaster cooker. £360. Same as York without back boiler.
Picardy. £300. Output up to 5½ kW. H 33½", W 23", L 24".

Log Fires (Woodstoves) Ltd
24, Harrow Farm Estate, Froxfield, Marlborough, Wiltshire
Tel: Great Bedwyn 682

Two UK made stoves are available from Logfires and both are manufactured using ¼ inch steel.
The Marlborough can be a closed or open stove and the Gloucester is
closed only.

The Marlborough.

The Marlborough Combination Stove
£249.48. Back boiler £54. Output 3/9 kW. 18" logs, H 25", W 24",
Depth 16".

The Gloucester Cottage Stove
£219.78. Back boiler £54. Output 2/8 kW. 20" logs, H 27", W 24",
Depth 13".

The Salisbury Arc
Room heater with central heating, available from September 1979.
About £370. Output 4½/5 kW to room, 35,000 Btu to hot water.
H 33", W 33", Depth 16".

Light Air Workshop
Mafeking Place, Annan, Dumfriesshire, Scotland.

Light Air sell plans for building your own woodstove from converted
churns or drums. The plans cost £2.00 for the horizontal type, £2.00
for the verticle type and £1.50 for the sawdust burner.

Modern Fires Ltd
50, Brighton Road, Salfords, Surrey.
Tel: Horley 3924

Modern Fires are the principal importers of the Lange range of Danish
made stoves. The cast iron stoves are available in black as a standard col-
our or in red or green at extra cost.

Lange 6302K
Closed stove with arched smoke circulator on top with cooking area
in arch.
£330. Output up to 11 kW. 24" logs. H 50½", W 16", Depth 34".

Lange 6302A
A closed stove with hot plate.
£240. Output up to 8 kW. 24" logs. H 34", W16", Depth 34".

Lange 6303
A closed stove with smoke circulating arch and hotplate underneath.
£190. Output up to 6 kW. 18" logs. H 37½", W 16", Depth 25".

Lange 6303 A
A small closed woodstove.
£132. Output up to 4 kW. 18" logs, H 25", W 16", Depth 25".

Lange 6203
A tall rectangular closed stove.
£195. Output up to 5 kW. 17" logs. H 35½", W 13½", Depth 20".

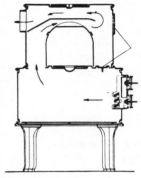

Lange 6302 K.   *Lange 6303.*

Lange 6204
A tall rectangular closed stove.
£225. Output up to 6.5 kW. 20" logs. H 35½", W 13½", Depth 24½".

Lange 909
A wood and coal burning cooker with oven and two hotplates.
£195. Output up to 5 kW.

Lange 911N
Wood and coal burning cooker as 909.
£280. Output up to 6 kW.

Lange 911W
An improved version of the previous model.
£320.

Lange 1620
A tall barrel-like open or closed stove, will burn wood and coal.
£280. Output up to 9 kW. 14" logs. H 35½", Diameter 19".

Passat Central Heating Ltd
6—8, College Street, Petersfield, Hants. GU31 4AD
Tel: Petersfield 4508

As well as the Passat multi-fuel boilers (see under Multi-fuel Section for
details) Passat also manufacture the P-77 woodburning stove/central
heater.
The P-77 is of double walled steel construction to allow hot air to circulate. It is also supplied with one or two back boilers which can supply
hot water and/or central heating.
It is equipped with glass doors so it can be enjoyed as an open or closed
stove.

Passat P-77
£380, extra with back boilers. Output 7/15 kW.

Peatol Woodburning Stoves
19, Knightlow Road, Harborne, Birmingham B17 8PS
Tel: 021-429 1015

Peatol produce three stoves made of 3/16 inch steel plate and finished in
matt black only. Models 24 and 36 may be fitted with a water jacket for
an additional £10.

Model No.18
£70. Approx heat output 4 kW. 14" logs. H 29", W 15", L 19",

Model No.24
£75. Approx heat output 6 kW. 20" logs. H 29", W 15", L 25".

Model No.36
£85. Approx heat output 8 kW. 32" logs. H 29", W 15", L 37".

Quebb Stoves
4, Market Street, Hay-on-Wye, Hereford.
Tel: Eardisley 338

Quebb manufacture a range of five solid woodstoves made from ¼ inch
boiler plate steel. The welded joints make the stoves airtight. All models
can be fitted with single or double hot water boilers to give domestic hot
water and central heating. The fire will stay in for at least 12 hours.
Available in matt black finish only. Quebb stoves are available direct
from the manufacturers only.

Small Quebb
£88. Output up to 3 kW. 12" logs. H 25", W 13½", L 14½". Boiler
£25 extra.

Medium Quebb
£92. Output up to 4/5 kW. 18" logs. H 25", W 13½", L 20½". Boiler
£25 extra.

Large Quebb
£105. Output up to 7 kW. 24" logs. H 27", W 13½", L 27½". Boiler
£25 extra.

Quebb Magnette
£115. H 27", W 16½", L 20½". Boiler £25 extra.

Quebb 7 kW Magnette with boilers.

Quebb Magnum
£125. Output up to 10 kW. 24" logs. H 27", W 16½", L 27½".

Smith & Wellstood Ltd
Bennybridge, Sterlingshire. PK4 2AP
Tel: 032 481 271

Smith & Wellstood manufacture the decorative Dragon woodburning
stove in cast iron, fitted with doors and mica windows so that it may
be used as an open or closed stove.

The Smith and Wellstood Dragon Stove.

The Dragon Stove
£220 in black, other colours extra. Output as a closed stove up to 7 kW, as an open fire up to 3.5 kW. 18" logs. H 32", W 33½", Depth 22".
Smith & Wellstood also manufacture the Romesse bot-bellied workshop heaters fired by solid fuel. A range of cookers and solid fuel fires are also available.

The Smockery Woodburning Centre
High Street, Mayfield, Sussex
Tel: Mayfield 3296

As well as stocking a fine selection of stoves on show at their centre, the Smockery are UK agents for the Danish Morso range of open and closed woodstoves.

Fireplace 1122
£195. Free-standing open fireplace. H 32", W 19", Depth 27".

Laertes 6B
£180. Closed stove. 17" logs. H 24½", W 14", Depth 23½".
Cast iron, enamelled matt black.

Horatio 2B
£180. Similar to above except this model can also be used as an open fire. H 29", W 13", Depth 27½".

Hamlet
Similar to the 2B except that it has an arched smoke circulating section on top. The space beneath the arch may be used for cooking.
£240. H 41½", W 13", Depth 27½".

Gertrude 1B
£340. A large closed stove with hotplate.

Claudius 1BO
£340. Same as the 1B with an arched smoke circulating section on top.

Elsinore 1125
This cast iron stove may be used as a closed or open fire.
£325. H 42", W 29½", Depth 23".

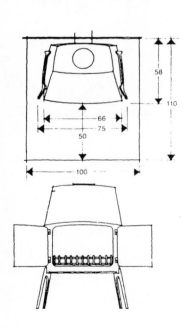

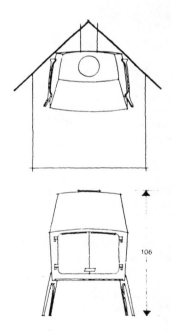

The Sherwood stove.

Philip Spencer Stoves Ltd
31, Market Square, Leighton Buzzard, Bedfordshire.
Tel: Leighton Buzzard 75048

Spencer Stoves make the Sherwood space heating stove.

Standard Sherwood Stove
£195. Output up to 10 kW. Cast iron with black finish, glass door.
18" logs.

Sherwood Stove with back boiler
£270. Same as above except supplied with a back boiler.

Strax Distribution Ltd.
416, Brecknock Road, London N7.
Tel: 01-485 7056

Strax are the main importers of the Ulefos cast iron woodstoves from
Norway where they have been in continuous production since 1657! They
are solid traditional stoves.

Ulefos No. 868
Box stove with hot plate. Black finish.
£112.50. 12" logs. 3 kW output. H 24½", W 11", L 19".

Ulefos 864.

Ulefos No. 864
Box stove with hot plate.
£135 black finish, £165 green enamel. Back boiler optional extra
£47.50.
4 kW output. 16" logs. H 26", W 13", L 20.5".

Ulefos No. 865
Box stove with hot plate.
£240 black finish., back boiler £52. 50 extra. 7kW output. 23.5" logs.
H.31", W 14", L 33".

Ulefos No. 172
A remarkable looking stove with double arched top and decorative
images cast in the sides.
£540. 8 kW output. 20" logs. H 68", W 13.5", L 31".

Ulefos No 105
A wood and coal burning free standing fireplace.
£255. 3 kW output.

Dovre Fireplace
The Dovre cast iron fireplace has an air convection chamber between
the unit and the wall. The air to be heated can be convected in from
the room or from outside. The fire is supplied with ornamental fire-
backs, legs, a base, grate, closed top and damper.
Large size £285 and small size £260.

Ellis Sykes & Son Ltd
Princes Street, Stockport, Cheshire.
Tel: 061 477 5626

Ellis Sykes distribute a wide range of wood and coal fired heaters, the
Godin cooker/boiler range, Bjorno stoves, Leda stoves and Spincraft
fireplaces.

Godin Cookers
This French made cooker also supplies central heating and domestic
hot water, and will operate on wood, coal and even oil when fitted
with a special burner. The comprehensive list of eight Godin cookers
give the optimum in choice. They are made of steel with cast iron
internal construction and have polished cast iron cooking surfaces on
top.
Rather than list all the details the range can be summarised by saying
that they are priced from £385 to £825. The cookers are sold in white
with chrome or copper trim.

Godin Stoves
Godin wood or coal fired stoves are made of cast iron and clad in enam-
elled steel. The fire is visible through the glass strip front window.
Nos. 3172 and 3170 have hot plates.

Godin Stove No. 3712
Brown or brown and sand colours.
£225. Output 24,000 Btu. 16" logs. H 25", W 28", Depth 16".

Godin Stove no 3710
Brown or brown and sand.
£330. Output 30,000 Btu. 19" logs. H 27", W 33", Depth 18".

Petit Godin
Stove No. 3720 £145.
Stove No. 3721 £180.

Godin Colonial
The Colonial is a cast iron Franklin style woodburning stove.
Colonial No. 3125 £190
Colonial No. 3126 £224
Colonial No. 3127 £244

Bjorno Woodstoves
Ellis Sykes import the Bjorno stoves made in Denmark. Boilers are available as optional extras with the models M and L. The stoves are made of
steel plate with firebrick lining and cased in stove enamelled steel. Air is

heated by circulating between the firebox and the casing, as such the Bjorno is a circulating stove.

Bjorno Model M
£204. Output up to 4.5 kW. 20" logs.

Bjorno Model L
£224. Output up to 5.5 kW. 20" logs.

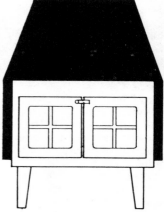

Spincraft Fireplaces
Ellis Sykes are also agents for the rather unusual range of Canadian Spincraft woodburning fireplaces. They are not intended to burn coal. Made of steel they come in five different colours.

The Starfire
This circular fireplace can be suspended by chains or be freestanding on its optional base. It has a roller screen and can be opened on three sides.
£242 basic cost.

The Onyx
The big log/fireplace. It has a rectangular shape and roller screen safety curtains.
£233 in matt black.

The Emerald
Same as the Onyx except it is a triangular shape to fit in corners.

The Zircon
This stove has a curved hood similar to the Jotul 7 except more squat.
£159 in black.

The Opal
This is shaped like a ball.
£186 in matt black.

Leda Stoves
The German company Leda make a range of four sturdy cast iron wood stoves.

Leda Workshop Heater
Small heater available in matt black.
£58. Output up to 2 kW.

Leda Cannon Stove
A fine example of the original pot-bellied stove.
£72. Output up to 2.5 kW.

Leda Box Stove
A plain box stove with two hot plates.
£88. Output up to 5 kW.

Leda Barbecue Stove
This remarkable stove is the ultimate if you want to have a wood-fired

Leda Barbecue Stove.

barbecue. It comes on wheels, has its own stovepipe and is made of
black enamelled cast iron.
£195 complete with all cooking accessories. 5 kW output for heating,
rotating spit, frying and barbecue.

Simon Thorpe Ltd
New Road, Newcastle Emlyn, Dyfed, Wales
Tel: 0239 710100

Simon Thorpe is the sole importer of Norwegian made Jotul stoves.
Long held to be the finest in woodstoves the Jotul is made of ¼ inch
cast iron and is designed to burn around the clock. Approximately
half of all stoves sold today are Jotul. Choose the right sized Jotul
and it will be a beautiful addition to your home.

Jotul 602
A small stove with hot plate. Front combustion, the logs burn like
a cigar. In matt black+green enamel.
£124. Output up to 4.5 kW. 16" logs. H 15", W 13", L 19".

Jotul 602.

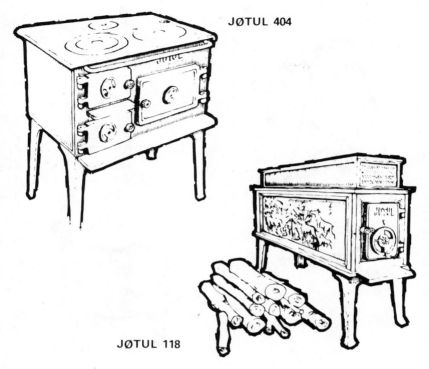

JØTUL 404

JØTUL 118

Jotul 380
A stove with two hot plates, can boil a kettle within 7—10 minutes of lighting. Matt black.
£140. Output up to 6 kW. 20'' logs. H 27½'', W 16'', L 32''.

Jotul 606
An unusual stove with an arch-like heat exchanger on top of the firebox. Cooking surface inside the arch. Black only.
£194. Output up to 6 kW. 18'' logs. H 41'', W 12½'', L 22½''.

Jotul 118
Heater for big rooms. Will boil kettle and smoke fish, chicken etc. Water heating kit available. Matt back/green enamel.
£203. Output up to 7 kW. 27'' logs. H 30'', W 14'', L 30''.

Jotul 404 Kitchen Stove
This cookstove will burn any solid fuel, and operates well on wood. One small and two large hotplates. Oven will take a standard sized chicken or three loaves of bread. Black enamel.
£241, Output up to 5 kW. 13'' logs. H 31'', W 24'', L 17''.

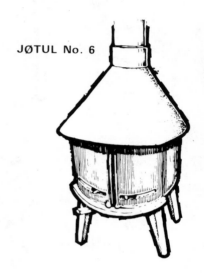

JØTUL No. 6

JØTUL No. 7

Jotul No.1

Combined open fire and slow combustion stove when the stove doors are closed — the best of both worlds. Will also burn coal in a special fire-basket. Matt black.
£247. Output, open fire up to 5 kW, closed stove 8.5 kW. 14½" logs. H 34", W 19", Depth 20".

Jotul No.7

The No. 7 in the right setting is an elegant and striking free-standing open fireplace with a conical top standing on a ciruclar fire base. Cast iron hood with sheet steel conical hood. Matt black.
£265. Output up to 4 kW. 24" logs. H 50", diameter 31½".

Jotul No. 6

Combined open fire and closed stove. Water heater kit available. Matt black.
£349. Output up to 11 kW. 14" logs. H 44", W 30", Depth 23½".

U. A. Engineering Ltd
Canal Street, Sheffield S4 7ZE
Tel: 0742 21167

U.A. Engineering import the French made Franco Belge stoves
and cookers.

The Woodburner
Designed to burn wood only, cast iron hearth. Finished in chocolate
and brown enamel. Hinged top with hotplate underneath.
£115. Output up to 6 kW. 18" logs. H 14", W 7", L 18".

The Ebene
Wood and coal burner. Pyrex glass window in front. Black finish.
£175. 15" logs. H 27½", W 23½", Depth 14".

The Economique
Basically the same as the Ebene, except without window and
available in two colours.
£140.

Franco Belge also manufacture a range of three cookers which
provide hot water and central heating. The cookers will burn wood and
coal. The main construction is of steel plate with cast iron top plate.

Franco Belge Cookers

Model 1703
£493. Output 10 kW. Approx 6 radiators. H 31½", W 31½", Depth 25".

Model 1705
£610. Output 14.5 kW. Approx 10 radiators. H 31½", W 35½",
Depth 29½".

Model 1707
£715. Output 19.5 kW. Approx 15 radiators. H 31½", W 39½",
Depth 32".

Wade Lewis Ltd
Stewart House, Brook Way, Kingston Road, Leatherhead, Surrey,
KT22 7LY

Wade Lewis manufacture the Forrester coal and wood burning stove
made from welded steel plate. The hinged doors, with glass windows,
enable the Forrester to be used either as an open or closed stove.

Forrester Stove.

Forrester Stove
£150 in black, brown or green, extra for other colours. Bottom grate £25 extra. Output up to 5 kW. H 32", W 29", L 18".

Waterford Ironfounders Ltd
Bilberry, Waterford, Ireland.

Waterford Ironfounders manufacture two Reginald box stoves and two Stanley cookers. They expect in late '78 to have a new woodstove which will take 2 ft logs, has a hot air blower and a back boiler.

Reginald 101
The 101 is a cast iron box stove.
£116. Output up to 4.5 kW. 16" logs. H 25", W 13", L 20".

Reginald 102
The Reginald 102 is just the same as the Jotul 118 in that it has a section on the top for smoking fish etc.
£206. Output up to 7 kW. 24" logs. H 30½", W 13½", L 31½".

Reginald 101 (left) and Reginald 102 (right).

Stanley Cooking Range
The Stanley cast iron cooker looks antiquated but is airtight. Two hot plates and an oven big enough for a 25 lb turkey. Wood or peat burning. £358. 16" logs. H 54½", W 35½", L 24". Black finish.

Stanley Cooker/Boiler
This cooker will burn any solid fuel, it will heat a 30 gallon cylinder and up to 140 sq. ft of radiator surface. Four hot plates. White enamel finish. £416. H 48½", W 36", L 21¾".

Waterford Ironfounders UK distributor is:-

Mr. J. R. Hayes, M.A. Buckley (Eng) Ltd., New Cut Industrial Estate, Woolston, Warrington, WA1 4AQ

Woodburning Stoves Co.Ltd.
Swerford Park, Oxfordshire. OX7 4 AU
Tel: Hook Norton 7845

Woodburning Stoves are UK agents for the French made Coste room heaters and cookstove. The two rectangular room heaters are made of steel.

Coste Heaters

Coste 98
£85. 15" logs. H 18¼", W 12½", L 20".

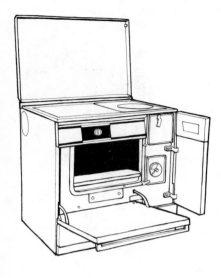

Coste Kitchen Stove.

Coste 99
£99. 15" logs. H 22½", W 13½", L 22½".

Coste Kitchen Stove
For cooking and water heating. Made of steel and cast iron. Will heat up to two radiators. Will also burn coal. White enamel finish. £350. Output up to 9 kW. 12" logs. H 31½", W 23½", L 31½".

Yorkpark Ltd
Woodbridge, Chequers lane, Preswood, Bucks. HP16 9DR
Tel: Great Missenden 4072

Yorkpark are UK agents for the Norwegian range of Trolla box stoves and wood cookers.

Trolla Box Stoves
The box stoves are available in matt black finish, the 103 and 104 are also available in green enamel. All have hot plates. Back boilers are available with some Trolla stoves.

Trolla 103
£97. Output 2.3 kW. 12", H 24½", W 11½", L 18".

Trolla 104
£119. Output 3-4.5 kW. 18" logs. H 25", W 12½", L 22½".

Trolla 108
£251. Ouput 7 kW. 27" logs. H 28½", W 13", L 31".

Trolla Cookers
The Trolla 325 has two large hot plates, the 354 has in addition a good sized oven. The cookers are designed to burn either coal or wood.

Trolla 325
£137. H 15¾", W 21½", L 14",

Trolla 354
£262. H 24¾", W 29", L 18".

Trolla Fireplace
With its hinged doors the fireplace model 810 has the advantages of a closed stove and an open fire. Available in black or green and black. £291. Output up to 6 kW. H 41½", W 25½", L 19".

Index of Manufacturers Part Two – Multi-Fuel Central Heaters

INDEX

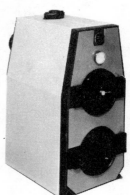

The Claremont.

Acoustics & Envirometrics Ltd
Ruxley Towers, Claygate, Surrey KT10 0UF
Tel: Esher 67281

A.E.L. import a range of six solid fuel boilers from Italy, all made of cast iron. Output ranges from 30 to 63 kW.
Called the Claremont, it is supplied only through the heating and ventilating trade. Write to A.E.L. for details of local availability.

Farm 2000 Ltd
15, Hazel Bank, Kings Norton, Birmingham B38 8BT
Tel: 021 459 6909

The Uni-boiler made by Farm 2000 will burn any solid fuel to supply hot water and central heating. Gas and oil-fired attachments cannot be supplied but the system works well in conjunction with an existing unit.
Details of the Farm 2000 Uni-boiler are as follows:-

Model	Output Btu/hr	Price
A3	80,000 – 120,000	£675
A4	120,000 – 160,000	£770
A6	160,000 – 220,000	£1065
A7	220,000 – 300,000	£1225

Farm 2000 Uni-boiler.

Le Feu de Bois Ltd
29, Clifden Road, Twickenham, Middx. TW1 4LU

This firm imports two multi-fuel central heating boilers, the De Dietrich and the Samat.

Passat Central Heating Ltd
6/8, College Street, Petersfield, Hants GU31 4AD

Passat, of Danish design, offers multi-fuel boilers for wet radiator and hot air central heating. Passat also manufacture a range of oil-fired boilers with a remarkable efficiency of 90%.

Passat Water Jacket Boilers

Model	Output Btu/hr	Price
HO-20	72,000	£385
HO-45	152,000	£555
HO-60	260,000	£885
HO-100	480,000	£1,295

*Passat
multi-fuel boiler.*

Passat Hot Air Boilers

Model	Output Btu/hr	Price
HOL-20	88,000	£595
HOL-45	200,000	£1,165

Passat are distributed in Ireland by Trim Central Heating, Trim, County Meath. Telephone 046 31167

Passat HOL units—
for hot air heating used to heat the immediate surroundings, or carrying hot air through ducts to other areas, these models are ideally suited to the woodworking and joinery industries, and for greenhouse heating.

Hot air models can have a supplementary oil burner fitted to start automatically when needed (HOLO).

Scanfield Boilers Ltd
'Herring Hang', Windmill Street, Hythe, Kent CT21 6BH
Tel: Hythe 65304

Like the Passat the Scanfield is also imported from Denmark. Gas and oil burners are optional fittings to the basic solid fuel burner, except on models 1 and 4.5. Details as follows:-

Model	Output Btu/hr	Price
1	60,000	£315
4.5	132,000	£680
5	180,000	£850
6	200,000	£1,283
10	320,000	£1,832
15	490,000	£2,196
20	650,000	£2,791

Ellis Sykes & Son Ltd
Victoria Works, Howard Street, Stockport, Cheshire
Tel: 061 477 5626

Another Danish model the Bjorno Model CH60 will burn wood, coal
and peat but unlike most other multi-fuel boilers it is not big enough
to take bales of straw.
Output 60,000 Btu. £330.

Bjorno CH 60/80 Boiler.

Simon Thorpe Ltd
New Road, Newcastle Emlyn, Dyfed, Wales
Tel: 0239 710100

Simon Thorpe, of Jotul woodstove fame, is preparing to import two
multi-fuel boilers to be marketed in the autumn of '78. Details not yet
available.

R. Tomlinson (Boilers) Ltd
Lotherton Way, Aberford Road Trading Estate, Garforth, Leeds.
Tel: Leeds 861122

The HS Farm range of multi-fuel boilers are of Danish design, some
models are manufactured in the UK by Tomlinson's and others are
imported.
The Otley OT range will operate on gas, oil, electricity, wood and waste
but it will not handle large items such as straw bales. Two combustion
chambers are linked, like the Passat, so that when the solid fuel burns
low the oil/gas burner takes over. Electric heating elements can be installed in tappings provided.

Otley OT Boilers

Model	Output Btu/hr on solid fuel	Price
OT-28	72,000	£604
OT-35	112,000	£671
OT-50	140,000	£765
OT-70	200,000	£925

Otley Type A
Will burn straw bales, wood and waste.

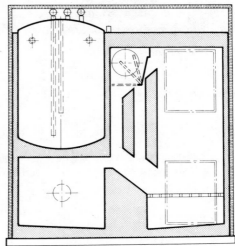

*Section diagram of Otley
OT boiler. Left-hand com-
bustion chamber is for oil
or gas firing, and the right-
hand chamber is for solid
fuel. Primary water (shaded
area) surrounds both com-
bustion chambers on all
sides to encourage heat
transfer, and the stainless
steel hot water cylinder
(upper left) is also im-
mersed in primary water.*

The Otley OT boiler/cylinder unit.

Model	Output Btu/hr	Price
A-16	80,000	£387
A-35	160,000	£620

As well as the OT and Type A which are probably of most interest to readers, Tomlinson also carry a more varied range of HS Farm boilers:-

Model	Fuel				
	Oil	*Gas*	*Electricity*	*Wood*	*Straw*
Jubilee	*	*		*	
Europa O	*	*		*	
Europa B	*	*		*	
Dover FT				*	
Midland MB	*	*	*	*	

U.A. Engineering Ltd
Canal Street, Sheffield, S4 7ZE
Tel: 0742 21167

U.A. Engineering import the Franco Belge range of five wood and coal central heating boilers. Models 93-27 and 93-40 can both be adapted to burn oil but not straw. The cookers listed earlier will also provide central heating and hot water.

Model	Output Btu/hr	Price
90-05	35,000	£377
90-09	52,000	£428
90-13	70,000	£499
93-27 (Le Forestiere)	108,000	£675
93-40 (Le Forestiere)	160,000	£770

The Franco Belge 1707 Central Heating Cooker (see page 79)